THIS WALKER BOOK BELONGS TO:

**To Thomas Shipman
with love**
P.P.

To my mum
I.A.

First published 1994 by Walker Books Ltd
87 Vauxhall Walk, London SE11 5HJ

This edition produced 2001 for The Book People Ltd,
Hall Wood Avenue, Haydock, St Helens WA11 9UL

2 4 6 8 10 9 7 5 3 1

Text © 1994 Peter Patilla
Illustrations © 1994 Ivan Allen

This book has been typeset in Flora.

Printed in Great Britain by Cox & Wyman Ltd, Reading, Berkshire

British Library Cataloguing in Publication Data
A catalogue record for this book is
available from the British Library.

ISBN 0-7445-7202-9

NUMBER PUZZLES

Written by
Peter Patilla

Illustrated by
Ivan Allen

GREETINGS! I AM
SKY MASTER. I NEED YOU
TO GO ON A DANGEROUS
MISSION FOR ME...
A MISSION THROUGH TIME,
A MISSION THROUGH SPACE,

**A MISSION
IN A MILLION!**

TED SMART

THE YEAR IS 2994 AD. THE PLACE IS COSMIC KINGDOM 6.
I, SKY MASTER, AND MY BROTHER, PLANET PRINCE, ARE THE
RULERS OF COSMIC KINGDOM 6. OUR UNCLE, SHADOW LORD,
IS JEALOUS. HE HAS PUT A SPELL ON PLANET PRINCE
AND TAKEN HIM TO HIS PALACE ON SATURN.

THE ONLY WAY TO BREAK SHADOW LORD'S MAGIC
IS FOR AN EARTH CHILD TO TRAVEL THROUGH
TIME AND FETCH THE **SOURCE CRYSTAL**...

WILL **YOU** BE THE BRAVE ONE? MY FRIEND,
WISE MONKEY, CAN GO WITH YOU TO HELP.
I WILL STAY HERE TO GUARD THE KINGDOM.

Me
(Sky Master)

Planet Prince

Wise Monkey

WHAT YOU MUST DO

1. There are 5 Rune Stones hidden in 5 different times. You must find all of them to reach the Source Crystal.

2. To find each Rune Stone you must solve the puzzles you come to along the way. Use a pencil and a calculator to help you.

3. Each Rune Stone has a date on it. That is the year you must go to next. I will zap you there automatically with my Time Gun.

4. The date on the fifth Rune Stone is the year in which the Source Crystal is hidden. Bring it back here safely and Shadow Lord's magic will be broken and my brother freed!

GOOD LUCK, BRAVE ONE!

Shadow Lord

YOU (Draw your picture here, Brave One)

65,000,000 BC

... YOU ARE TRAVELLING BACK IN TIME TO THE YEAR 65,000,000 BC WHEN DINOSAURS ROAMED THE EARTH AND HUMANS DID NOT EXIST! YOUR MISSION HAS BEGUN, BRAVE ONE!

To find out what the dinosaurs want to eat, solve the sums written beside the dots. Then join the dots in the order of your answers.

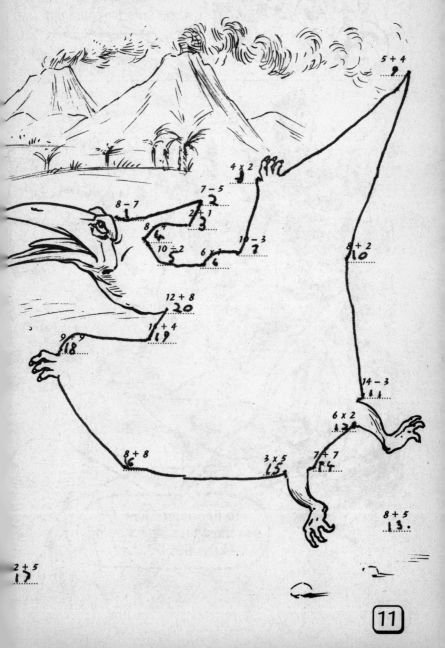

5 + 4

4 x 2

7 − 5
2

8 − 7
1

2 + 1
3

8
4

10 − 3
7

10 ÷ 2
5

6 x 1
6

8 + 2
10

12 + 8
20

15 + 4
19

9 + 9
18

14 − 3
11

6 x 2
12

8 + 8
16

3 x 5
15

7 + 7
14

8 + 5
13

2 + 5
7

11

To find the right way across the Swamp Maze, first solve the sums in the column with your calculator. Then, follow the answers across the swamp in that order. As you go, collect the letters you land on and write them in the boxes below. They will spell out what to do next.

G O   T O   S T O N E   C A V E

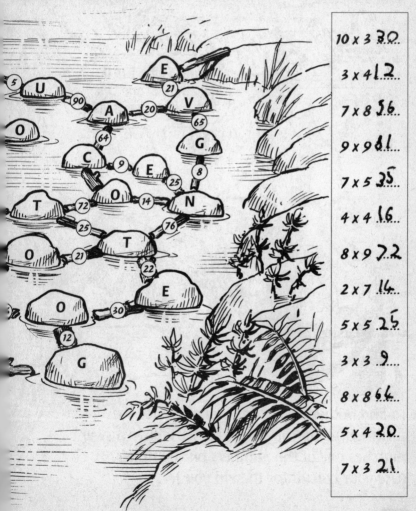

10×3 30

3×4 12

7×8 56

9×9 81

7×5 35

4×4 16

8×9 72

2×7 14

5×5 25

3×3 9

8×8 64

5×4 20

7×3 21

To find out which is Rune Stone 1, solve the sums written in the sand and see which answer matches one of the numbers on the stones. (Use your calculator to help you.)

15

... NOW YOU MUST FIND RUNE STONE 2.

King Arthur has been captured! To rescue him from the Black Knight's army, Brave One, you must find his magic weapons.

The odd shield out is the magic one. Can you spot it?

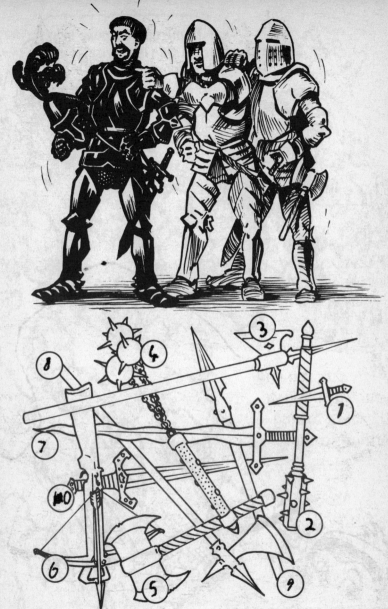

In what order should you pick up these weapons to reach King Arthur's magic sword? Write your answers in the circles. The first one has been done for you.

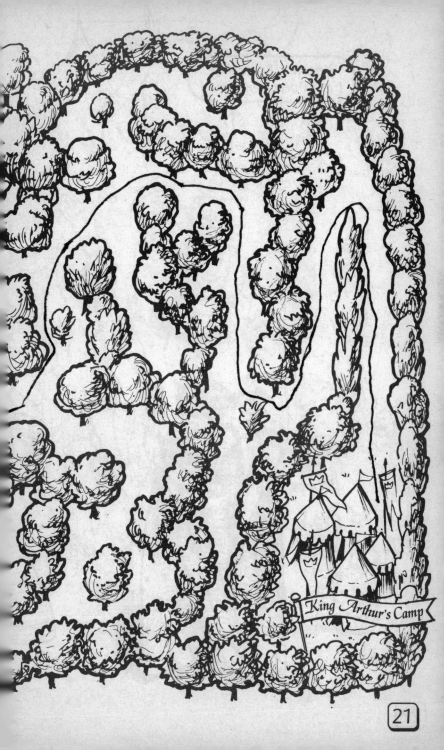

King Arthur's Camp

... A YEAR IN THE REIGN OF QUEEN CLEOPATRA.

Help the camel driver cross the river to reach her animals by joining the dots with **even numbers only**.

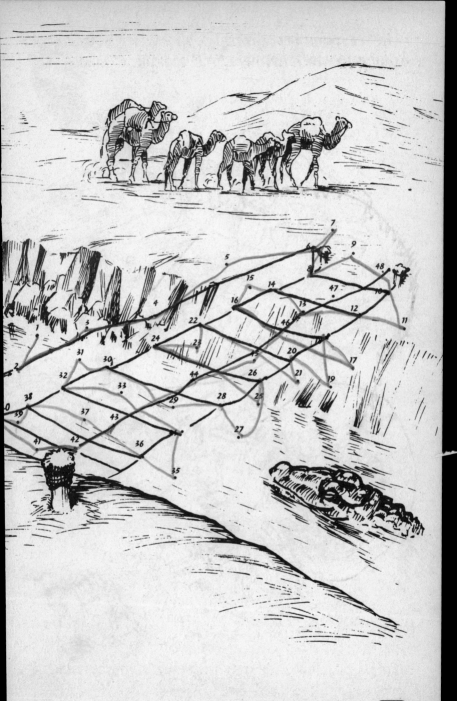

27

Help her round her camels up. Spot which baby camel belongs to which mother camel to make 6 pairs.

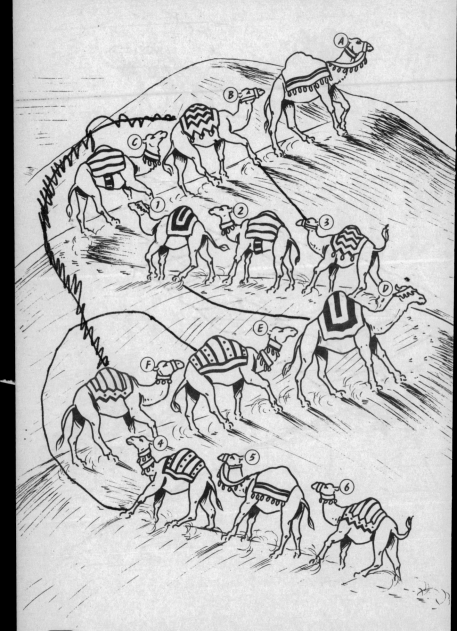

To enter the pyramid, complete the numbers on the blocks. Every number is the sum of the 2 numbers directly below it. Can you work it out?

To find Cleopatra,
you must trace a route through the
Mummy Maze without crossing any lines.

30

Can you crack the code and
work out what year is written on the stone?

Write it here: 2 9 9 4 A D

You have landed on an asteroid near Saturn. Find out what vehicle will take you to the planet by joining the dots with **odd numbers only**.

FINISH

START

35

First, crack the pass code to the palace doors by untangling these numbers.

Write the answer in here.

Next, pull the lever that's the odd one out.

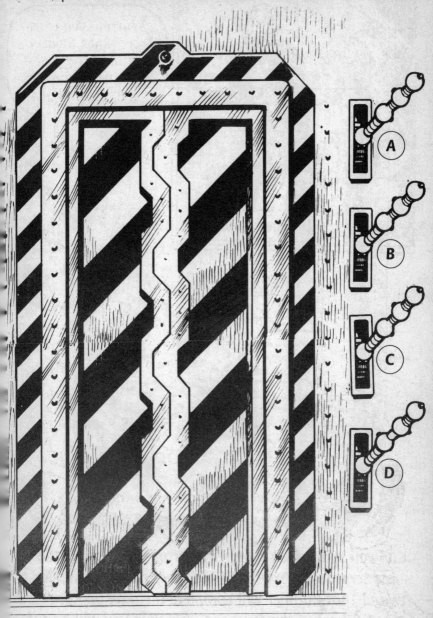

Can you spot which number appears only once in the Time Scramblers' rays? (All the other numbers appear twice.) That number will complete the date on Rune Stone 4 (behind Shadow Lord) and then you will be safe.

... RUNE STONE 5 IS IN THE YEAR 1685 AD — WHEN PIRATES ROAMED THE HIGH SEAS.

Can you read the writing on the wall? The letters are in the right order, but the spaces between them are wrong.

The Captain's cabin has 3 locks.
Can you find 3 keys in the picture?

To free the captain, you must spot 10 perils in this room. Rune Stone 5 is also here. Can you find it? What date is on it?

... THE SOURCE CRYSTAL IS HIDDEN IN THE TIME OF THE WILD WEST!

51

Follow Wild Billy, Brave One. He'll lead you to the Source Crystal.

Can you find the right way across the desert?

Wild Billy and his friend Big Chief Gently Running River are the guardians of the Source Crystal. Together they have kept the secret safe...

Can you spot 20 differences between this picture and the one on the opposite page? One of the differences will reveal the Source Crystal.

57

ANSWERS

PAGE 7

Leftover numbers spell:
65,000,000 BC

PAGE 11

PAGE 13
Answers to sums in column:
**30, 12, 56, 81, 35, 16,
72, 14, 25, 9, 64, 20, 21**
Right way across
Swamp Maze spells:
GO TO STONE CAVE

PAGE 15
Sums in sand:
353 + 6 = 359
492 − 30 = 462
218 + 5 = 223
593 − 81 = 512
399 + 112 = 511
Matching answer: **511**

PAGE 18
E is the odd shield out.

PAGE 19

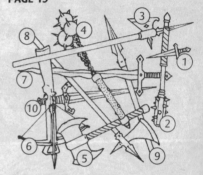

PAGES 20 AND 21

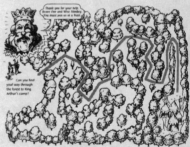

PAGE 23
Answer to Merlin's sum:
25 (BC)

PAGE 27

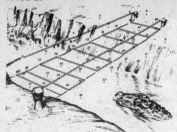

PAGE 28
A5, B3, C2, D1, E4, F6

PAGE 29

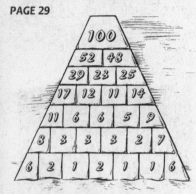

PAGE 30

PAGE 31
2994 AD

PAGE 34

PAGE 35

PAGE 36
Pass code: **1956**

PAGE 37
D is the odd one out.

PAGES 38 AND 39
Number that only appears once:
16
Date on Rune Stone 4: **1685** AD

PAGES 42 AND 43

PAGE 44

Rope **3** has an even number of knots.
Writing on wall:
THE RUNE STONE IS IN THE
TREASURE CHEST

PAGE 45

PAGES 46 AND 47

Date on Rune Stone 5: **1857** AD

PAGE 51

Wild Billy is the second from
the back.

PAGE 52

PAGE 55